LUDWIG VAN BEETHOVEN

PIANO CONCERTO No. 1

C major/C-Dur/Ut majeur
Op. 15

Ernst Eulenburg Ltd

London · Mainz · Madrid · New York · Paris · Prague · Tokyo · Toronto · Zürich

CONTENTS

BEETHOVEN'S CONCERTO PRODUCTION: COMPOSITION, PERFORMANCE, PUBLICATION
BEETHOVENS KONZERTSCHAFFEN: DATEN DER ENTSTEHUNG, URAUFFÜHRUNG, VERÖFFENTLICHUNG

	Title and key/ Titel und Tonart	(Preliminary) principal dates of composition/ (Entwürfe) Haupt-Kompositionsdaten	First performance/ Uraufführung	First edition/ Erstausgabe (as orch. Parts)	Dedication/ Widmung
Op.19	Piano Concerto No.2, B♭	begun before 1793; rev.1794, 1798	29 March 1795 Vienna	Leipzig, 1801	Carl Nicklas von Nickelsberg
Op.15	Piano Concerto No.1, C	1795; ?rev. 1800	18 Dec 1795 Prague	Vienna, 1801	Fürstin Barbara Odescalchi (née Gräfin von Keglevics)
Op.37	Piano Concerto No.3, C	?1800	5 April 1803 Vienna	Vienna, 1804	Fürst Louis Ferdinand von Preußen
Op.56	Triple Concerto, C Pfte, Vln, Vc, Orch	1803–4	May 1808 Vienna	Vienna, 1807	Fürst Franz Joseph von Lobkowitz
Op.58	Piano Concerto No.4, G	1805–6	March 1807 Vienna	Vienna, 1808	Erzherzog Rudolph von Österreich
Op.61	Violin Concerto, D	1806	23 Dec 1806 Vienna	Vienna, 1808 London, 1810	Stephan von Breuning
Op.73	Piano Concerto No.5, E♭ ('Emperor')	1809	?28 Nov 1811 Leipzig	London, 1810 Leipzig, 1811	Erzherzog Rudolph von Österreich

(List excludes fragments, incomplete works, and soloistic works not titled 'Concerto'/Die Liste beinhaltet keine Fragmente, unvollendete Werke oder solistische Stücke, die nicht mit ''Konzert'' betitelt sind.)

PREFACE

As the first entirely new and splendid effects on this instrument, Beethoven discovered a much more difficult variety, just as was the sonorous and cantabile style. He had, as he often said, practised day and night in his youth […]. As regards his brilliance and the inspired freedom of his playing no one at that time equalled him,[1]

thus reported Carl Czerny of the appearance of Ludwig van Beethoven, who had come to Vienna in 1792 and subsequently to become Czerny's own teacher. That the composer wrote particularly for *his* instrument, the piano, was natural. Already in 1784 – thus still in his Bonn period – Beethoven had written a piano concerto in E flat major WoO 4, in Vienna, a rondo in B flat major WoO 6 and the concerto in B flat major which is known as the second piano concerto Op. 19. Only later – probably in 1795/ 96 – did he then begin the concerto in C major, the present 'No. 1' that he finished in 1798. The confusing numbering can be put down to the fact that the composer first of all published this work – once more revised – in March 1801 (as a set of parts, without score) with the title 'Grand Concert pour le Piano-Forte' and dedication to the Princess Barbara Odescalchi; the B flat major concerto followed in December of the same year. (The E flat major work of his youth was not counted in the canon of the five Beethoven Piano Concertos, neither was his arrangement of the Violin Concerto in D major Op. 61a.)

The composer probably first played his work from the manuscript on 29 March 1795 as part of an academy in Vienna, his first public appearance in his new hometown, then in 1798 in an academy put on by Beethoven in the Konviktsaal at Prague. That in his own opinion, according to a letter of 22 April 1801 to the publishing house Breitkopf & Härtel, this work – as also the B flat major concerto – 'still did not belong amongst my best of the kind',[2] possibly had to do with the fact that he wanted to 'show off' his third concerto in C minor Op. 37 a little. On the other hand, 'musical politics' so Beethoven said, calls for 'keeping the best concerto for oneself for a time'[3] – thus an economic viewpoint is bound to enter in, because what is not published cannot profitably be played by others.

If the first piano concerto in B flat major – once the youthful Bonn work is left out of consideration – is still clearly in the tradition, the C major work is marked by a slow breaking away from previous models, especially those of Mozart. The scoring is larger and weightier, the formal framework broadened and demands on the pianist increased. A more virtuosic and festively self-proclaiming character influenced the opening movement *Allegro con brio*. Bracing harmonic effects and contrasts provide for surprises, for example, when the middle movement, a lyrical *Largo*, is in the third-related key of A flat major. The playful and humorous rondo, an *Allegro scherzando*, rounds off the work with

[1] Quotation from 'Weitere Erinnerungen an Beethoven', in: Carl Czerny, *Erinnerungen aus meinem Leben*, ed. and annotated by Walter Kolneder (Strasbourg, Baden-Baden, 1968), 45

[2] Quotation from Alexander Wheelock Thayer, *Ludwig van Beethovens Leben*. Adapted in German from the original manuscript by Hermann Deiters, Vol. 2 (Leipzig, 1910), 240

[3] ibid., 240

virtuosity. The original cadenza and those originating later give a small insight into both the technical playing skills and the art of improvisation, praised time and again, of Ludwig van Beethoven.

virtuosity. The original cadenza and those originating later give a small insight into both the technical playing skills and the art of improvisation, praised time and again, of Ludwig van Beethoven.

Contemporary critics did not exactly react exuberantly to the first piano concerto. Thus, the Leipzig *Allgemeine Musikalische Zeitung* reported in 1804 on a performance in Berlin:

A new fortepiano concerto by Beethoven, furnished with chromatic passages and enharmonic confusion now and then to the point of bizarreness, concluded the first section. The solo part was very difficult

– even if it was well mastered by the interpreter and very precisely accompanied by the orchestra.

The first movement was splendidly worked: yet the modulations run riot altogether too much; the Adagio in A flat major was an extremely pleasant, richly melodic piece […] The last [sic!] movement: All'Inglese, was distinguished only by unusual rhythms […][4]

That which rather displeased his contemporaries, is in retrospect regarded as refreshingly innovative.

Wolfgang Birtel
Translation: Margit McCorkle

[4] Quotation from *Ludwig van Beethoven. Die Werke im Spiegel seiner Zeit. Gesammelte Konzertberichte und Rezensionen bis 1830*, ed. with introduction by Stefan Kunze (Laaber, 1987), 20

VORWORT

Beethoven hat als erster ganz neue und groß-artige Effekte auf diesem Instrument entdeckt, eine viel schwierigere Spielart, ebenso wie den klangvollen und kantablen Stil. Er hatte, wie er oft sagte, in seiner Jugend Tag und Nacht geübt […]. Hinsichtlich seiner Brillanz und der genia-len Freizügigkeit des Spiels kam ihm damals niemand gleich,[1]

berichtet Carl Czerny vom Auftreten Ludwig van Beethovens, der 1792 nach Wien ge-kommen war und dann Lehrer von Czerny wurde. Dass der Komponist insbesondere für *sein* Instrument, das Klavier, schrieb, war selbstverständlich. Bereits 1784, also noch in seiner Bonner Zeit, schrieb Beet-hoven ein Klavierkonzert in Es-Dur, WoO 4, in Wien ein Rondo in B-Dur, WoO 6, und das Konzert in B-Dur, das als Opus 19 und als zweites Klavierkonzert firmiert. Erst später – wohl 1795/96 – begann er dann mit dem Konzert in C-Dur, dem heutigen „Nr. 1", das er 1798 beendete. Die verwir-rende Nummerierung ist darauf zurückzu-führen, dass der Komponist dieses – noch-mals überarbeitete – Werk (als Stimmensatz, also ohne Partitur) mit dem Titel „Grand Concert pour le Piano-Forte" und der Fürstin Barbara Odescalchi gewidmet im März 1801 als erstes veröffentlichte; das B-Dur-Konzert folgte im Dezember des gleichen Jahres. (Das Es-Dur-Jugendwerk zählt nicht zu dem Kanon der fünf Beet-hovenschen Klavierkonzerte, ebenso wenig wie seine Bearbeitung des Violinkonzertes in D-Dur, op. 61a.)

Der Komponist spielte sein Werk aus dem Manuskript erstmals – wahrschein-lich – am 29. März 1795 im Rahmen einer Akademie in Wien, seinem ersten öffent-lichen Auftreten in der neuen Heimat, dann 1798 in einer von Beethoven veranstalteten Akademie im Konviktsaal zu Prag. Dass nach seiner eigenen Meinung dieses – wie auch das B-Dur-Konzert – laut einem Brief vom 22. April 1801 an den Verlag Breit-kopf & Härtel „noch nicht unter meinen besten von der Art gehört"[2], hatte mögli-cherweise damit zu tun, dass er ein wenig „Reklame" für sein drittes Konzert in c-Moll, op. 37, machen wollte. Andererseits erfordere, so Beethoven, „die musikalische Politik die besten Concerte eine Zeitlang bei sich zu behalten"[3] – da stecken sicher-lich wirtschaftliche Gesichtspunkte dahin-ter, denn was nicht veröffentlicht ist, kann nicht von anderen gewinnbringend gespielt werden.

Steht das Erstlings-Klavierkonzert in B-Dur – sieht man von dem Bonner Jugendwerk einmal ab – noch deutlich in der Tradition, zeichnet sich beim C-Dur-Werk eine langsame Loslösung von den Vorbildern, insbesondere von demjenigen Mozarts ab. Die Besetzung ist größer und gewichtiger, der formale Rahmen gewei-tet und die Anforderung an den Pianisten gesteigert. Ein virtuoser und festlich auf-trumpfender Charakter bestimmt den Ein-gangssatz Allegro con brio. Harmonische Reizwirkungen und Kontraste sorgen für

[1] Zit. nach „Weitere Erinnerungen an Beethoven", in: Carl Czerny, *Erinnerungen aus meinem Leben*, hrsg. und mit Anmerkungen versehen von Walter Kolneder, Strasbourg, Baden-Baden 1968, S. 45.

[2] Zit. nach Alexander Wheelock Thayer, *Ludwig van Beethovens Leben*. Nach dem Original-Manu-skript deutsch bearb. von Hermann Deiters, Bd. 2, Leipzig 1910, S. 240.

[3] Ebda., S. 240.

Überraschungen, so auch, wenn der Mittelsatz, ein lyrisch getöntes Largo, in der terzverwandten Tonart As-Dur steht. Das spielerische und humorige Rondo, ein Allegro scherzando, setzt einen virtuosen Schlusspunkt unter das Werk. Die originalen und später entstandenen Kadenzen geben einen kleinen Einblick in die spieltechnischen Fertigkeiten und in die immer wieder gerühmte Improvisationskunst Ludwig van Beethovens.

Die zeitgenössische Kritik reagierte auf das erste Klavierkonzert nicht gerade überschwänglich. So berichtet die Leipziger *Allgemeine Musikalische Zeitung* 1804 von einer Aufführung in Berlin:

Ein neues, mit chromatischen Gängen und enharmonischen Verwechselungen zuweilen bis zur Bizarrerie ausgestattetes Fortepianokonzert von Beethoven, beschloss den ersten Theil. Die Soloparthie war sehr schwierig

– auch wenn sie vom Interpreten gut gemeistert und vom Orchester sehr genau begleitet wurde.

Der erste Satz war vortrefflich gearbeitet: doch schweifen die Modulationen allzusehr aus; das Adagio aus As dur war ein äusserst angenehmes, melodienreiches Stück [...] Der lezte [sic!] Satz: All'Inglese, zeichnete sich nur durch ungewöhnliche Rhythmen aus ...[4]

– was den Zeitgenossen eher missfiel, gilt in der Rückschau als das erfrischend Innovative.

Wolfgang Birtel

[4] Zit. nach *Ludwig van Beethoven. Die Werke im Spiegel seiner Zeit. Gesammelte Konzertberichte und Rezensionen bis 1830,* hrsg. und eingeleitet von Stefan Kunze, Laaber 1987, S. 20.

PIANO CONCERTO No. 1

Der Fürstin Barbara Odescalchi gewidmet

Ludwig van Beethoven
(1770–1827)
Op. 15

I

Allegro con brio

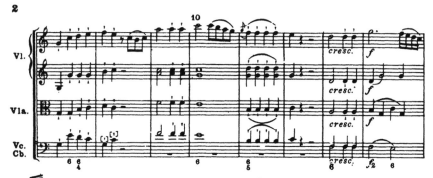

E. E. 3815

6

E.E. 3815

10

E. E. 3815

724-2   E. E. 3815

12

E. E 3815

14

16

E E.3815

170

20

E.E.3815

21

F.E. 3817

22

E. E. 3815

E.E.3815

26

E.E. 3815

28

E.E.3815

E.E. 3815

Fl.

Ob.

Fg.

Vl.

Vla.

Vc.
Cb.

Klav.

[staccato]

300

Fl.

Ob.

Fg.

Vl.

Vla.

Vc.
e Cb.

Klav.

32

34

E.E. 3815

85

E.E.3515

88

E.E.3815

40

E.E.3815

400

43

724-4 E.E.3815

44

E.E.3815

46

450

48

E.E. 3815

*) Originalkadenzen siehe im Anhang p. 109 ff.

II

56

E.E. 3815

E.E. 3815

59

724-5   E.E.3815

60

E.E. 3815

62

E.E. 3815

E.E. 3815

65

E. E. 3915

66

Cl.

Fg.

Cor.
(Es)

Vl.

Vla.

Vc.
Cb.

Klav.

Cl.

Fg.

Cor.
(Es)

Vl.

Vla.

Vc.
Cb.

Klav.

con Ped.

E. E. 3815

Rondo

III

Allegro scherzando

Flauto

2 Oboi

2 Clarinetti in C

2 Fagotti

2 Corni in C

2 Trombe in C

Timpani in C - G

Violino 1

Violino II

Viola

Violoncello
e
Contrabasso

Klavier

[p] [leggiermente]

Klav.

E. E. 3815

E.E. 3815

E.E.3815

72

E. E. 3815

74

E. E. 3815

E. E. 3915

E. E. 3815

78

E. E. 3815

E. E. 3815

82

85

E.E.3815

86

89

E. E.3815

724-7

E. E. 3815

92

724   E. E. 3815

94

E.E. 3815

E.E. 3815

98

E. E. 3815

102

E.E. 3815

560

Adagio

Tempo I.

E. E. 3815

Anhang
Kadenz zum ersten Satz (S.49)

(Fortsetzung fehlt)

Kadenz zum ersten Satz (S.49)

113

Kadenz zum ersten Satz (S.49)

118

E. E. 3815

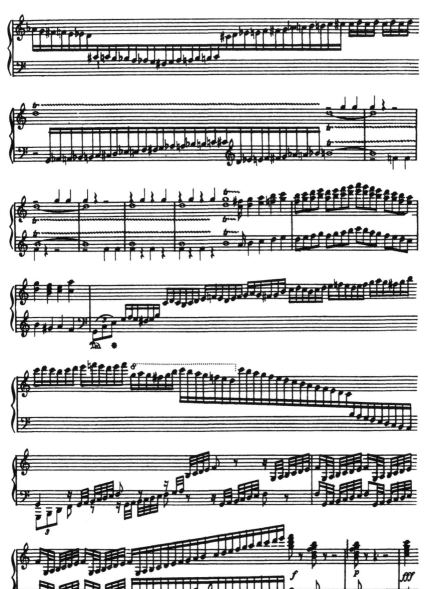

Kadenz zum dritten Satz (S. 98)